20,000 LEAGUES UNDER THE SEA

A GRAPHIC CLASSIC BY
ADAM GRANT AND TERRY M. WEST

BASED ON THE NOVEL BY
JULES VERNE

SCHOLASTIC INC.
New York Toronto London Auckland Sydney
Mexico City New Delhi Hong Kong

ENCILLER
GREG FOLLENDER

INKER
DAVID MOWRY

COLORIST
J. BROWN AND TECH FX

LETTERER
FRED VAN LENTE

COVER ARTIST
MICHAEL LILLY

COVER COLORS
J. BROWN AND TECH FX

Copyright © 1999 by Scholastic Inc.
All rights reserved. Published by Scholastic Inc.
Printed in the U.S.A.

ISBN 0-439-05672-1

SCHOLASTIC, READ 180, and associated logos and designs are
trademarks and/or registered trademarks of Scholastic Inc.
LEXILE is a trademark of MetaMetrics, Inc.

20 19 18 17 16 15 14 13 12   23   07

20,000 LEAGUES UNDER THE SEA

WHAT WILL THE FUTURE BE LIKE? WHAT NEW INVENTIONS WILL PEOPLE USE?

MANY SCIENCE FICTION WRITERS HAVE TRIED TO ANSWER THESE QUESTIONS. ONE OF THE MOST FAMOUS WAS JULES VERNE. HE HAD AN AMAZING ABILITY TO DREAM UP THE *RIGHT* ANSWERS.

ABOUT 100 YEARS AGO, VERNE WROTE <u>20,000 LEAGUES UNDER THE SEA</u>. IT TOLD OF A CRAZED INVENTOR NAMED CAPTAIN NEMO.

NEMO BUILT AN AMAZING SHIP THAT COULD TRAVEL UNDERSEA. ON BOARD WERE MANY INVENTIONS. THERE WAS A TANK THAT LET THE CREW BREATHE UNDERWATER. THERE WAS A MACHINE THAT MADE ELECTRICITY.

AT THE TIME, NEMO'S INVENTIONS WERE JUST DREAMS. NOW THEY'RE REAL.

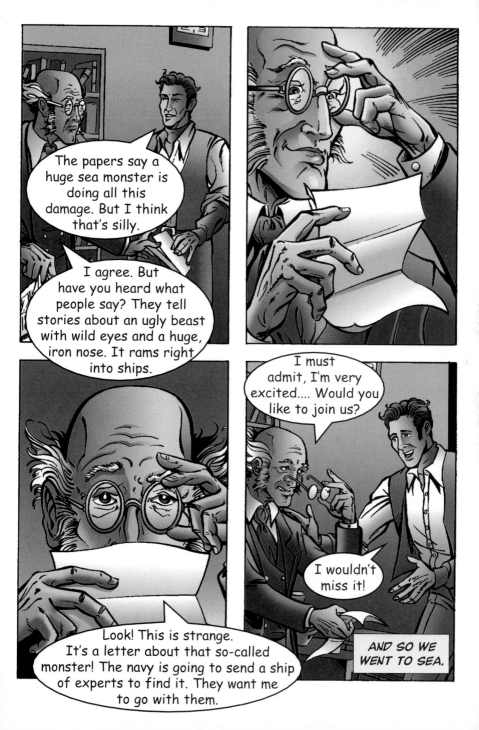

WE SEARCHED FOR MONTHS AND MONTHS.

BUT WE FOUND NOTHING.

FINALLY, ONE DAY, OUR CAPTAIN SPOKE TO THE CREW.

We must head for home—

JUST THEN ONE OF THE MEN, NED LAND, SPOTTED SOMETHING IN THE WATER.

Ahoy!!! It's the monster!!!

Men, get ready!

THE MONSTER WAS NOT MOVING. THE CREW THOUGHT IT WAS ASLEEP. WE MOVED TOWARD IT SLOWLY. NED GOT READY TO THROW HIS HARPOON.

THEN THE BEAST RUSHED AT US. IT HIT US VERY HARD. CONSEIL, NED, AND I FELL OUT OF THE SHIP.

I AWOKE IN THE OCEAN. I SAW OUR SHIP SAILING AWAY WITHOUT US. THEY HAD NOT SEEN US FALL OVERBOARD.

Help! Help! Come back!

Try to be calm, Professor!

THEN WE HEARD A VOICE. IT WAS NED.

Conseil! Professor! Up here!

Ned, have you killed the whale?

You won't believe it. But this whale is made of iron! Come aboard.

It looks like some kind of underwater ship! I've never seen one like it!

Who are you people?

A MOMENT LATER, A DOOR OPENED. A CREW OF MEN CAME OUT.

THEY FORCED US INTO THE SHIP ...

Get your hands off me!

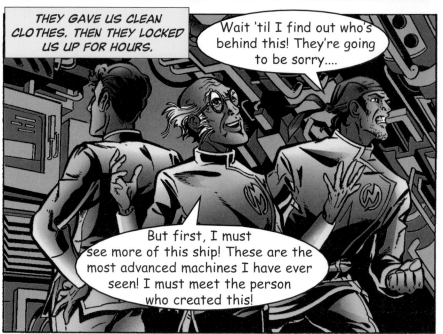

THEY GAVE US CLEAN CLOTHES. THEN THEY LOCKED US UP FOR HOURS.

Wait 'til I find out who's behind this! They're going to be sorry....

But first, I must see more of this ship! These are the most advanced machines I have ever seen! I must meet the person who created this!

WHAT NEMO SAID BOTHERED ME. BUT I PUT IT OUT OF MY MIND.

THE NEXT FEW MONTHS, WE HAD MANY AMAZING ADVENTURES.

WE TRAVELED ALL OVER THE WORLD. WE STUDIED THE SECRETS OF THE DEEP.

WE EVEN TRAVELED TO THE SOUTH POLE.

Don't worry, men. The *Nautilus* can cut through ice.

I WAS VERY INTERESTED IN EVERYTHING I SAW. BUT I COULDN'T FORGET THAT WE WERE PRISONERS. AND MY FRIENDS COULDN'T FORGET IT, EITHER.

I can't stay on this ship much longer.

We've got to find a way out of here.

I do not trust Nemo. We must escape soon.

I DECIDED TO TALK WITH NEMO ABOUT LETTING US GO.

Captain, could I speak with you? It's important.

Not now, Professor. I'm finishing my life story.

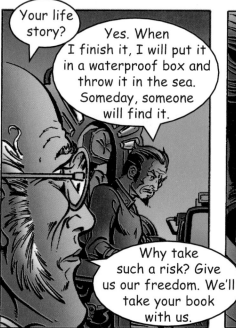

Your life story?

Yes. When I finish it, I will put it in a waterproof box and throw it in the sea. Someday, someone will find it.

Why take such a risk? Give us our freedom. We'll take your book with us.

Your freedom?!

I told you that no one may ever leave the *Nautilus!!!*

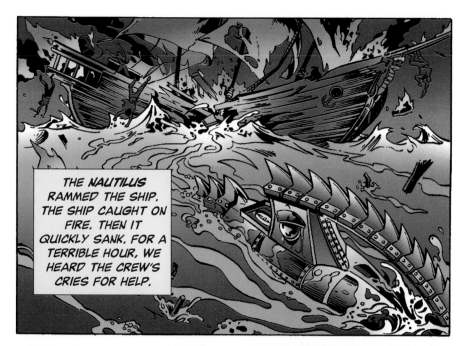

THE *NAUTILUS* RAMMED THE SHIP. THE SHIP CAUGHT ON FIRE, THEN IT QUICKLY SANK. FOR A TERRIBLE HOUR, WE HEARD THE CREW'S CRIES FOR HELP.

You killed those men!

I was only defending my ship and my crew.

I do not feel sad for them.

THAT NIGHT, THE *NAUTILUS* WAS STILL ON THE SURFACE.

WE KNEW IT WAS OUR CHANCE TO ESCAPE.

WE SNEAKED OUT AND GOT INTO ONE OF THE *NAUTILUS'S* LIFEBOATS.

Look!

SUDDENLY, THERE WAS A HUGE WHIRLPOOL. IT WAS SPINNING THE *NAUTILUS* AROUND.

A whirlpool! There are lots of them in these waters! They can drag a ship to the bottom and smash it into a million pieces!

SOMEHOW, WE ROWED OUT OF DANGER.

We're free!

BUT THE *NAUTILUS* WAS NOT AS LUCKY.

THE NEXT DAY, WE SAW LAND.

Land, ho!

WE NEVER FOUND OUT WHAT HAPPENED TO CAPTAIN NEMO....

MAYBE ONE DAY SOMEONE WILL FIND HIS BOOK. OR MAYBE HE AND HIS *NAUTILUS* ARE STILL TRAVELING ON THE BOTTOM OF THE SEA....